Letters from IGNORANTIA

Braxton Hunter

TRINITY LIVING PRESS

Trinity Living Press
(an affiliate of Trinity Academic Press)

ISBN-13: 978-0692698846

ISBN-10: 0692698841

Printed in the United States of America

Hunter, Braxton, 2019-
Letters from Ignorantia
Braxton Hunter.
p. cm.
ISBN-10: 1-7328963-1-3
ISBN-13: 978-1-7328963-1-4

1. Satire - Fiction. 2. Theology - Bible.
3. Religion. 1. Title.

---

10 9 8 7 6 5 4 3 2 1

For

Johnathan and Misty

CONTENTS

INTRODUCTION

From where have these letters come? Did I find them stuffed between the cinderblocks in the wall of my tiny hut in the Philippines back in 2007? Were they wrestled out of the rubble at the site of the church of Philadelphia when I visited modern Alaşehir last fall? Was it that impossibly old man I met in the Australian outback this past December? Did he give them to me, speaking of a different, but similar time and place? Maybe. Or maybe the persons, and places are fictions of my own imagination. It really makes no difference. Whether Ignorantia and Verum are real, or mere stand-ins for more familiar nations and cultures, the principles and ideas contained in these letters are important for our consideration.

I've endeavored to make the text more understandable for those of us who are neither from Ignorantia, nor Verum by opting for the New American Standard Bible translation where the authors of the letters may have used something else. Hopefully, this will not break the flow intended by the original correspondents. Also, I must note that the paragraph beginning on page twenty-six, and ending on page twenty-seven sounds very much like the work *Organizational Culture and Leadership*, by Edgar Schein. In case that's no coincidence, I felt it should be mentioned.

It is my belief that there are many great truths and insights found in this collection, but there are two overarching lessons that I hope shine through. First, I hope the reader is impressed with the understanding that becoming a Christian, while of the utmost importance, should be followed by a sincere, lifelong, relentless desire to understand God through the Scriptures. There may be, and often is, serious spiritual danger in simply adopting the group thinking of a particular denomination, congregation, figure, or book – *even this one!*

Secondly, the most knowledgeable of biblical students can fall into the enemy's snares precisely because of an arrogance regarding his or her theological and scriptural knowledge. If it is not clear in this body of text anywhere else, it should be noted emphatically here: *Whether one knows the Word well or not, one must know, love, and depend on the Savior!*

Having spent a great deal of time with both everyday Christians, and skilled seminarians, I humbly suggest the following on the basis of my observations: *Satan is just as satisfied with scholars who do not live the Scriptures as he is with the ignorant who do not know them!*

PART ONE

"The Word of God well understood and religiously obeyed is the shortest route to spiritual perfection. And we must not select a few favorite passages to the exclusion of others. Nothing less than a whole Bible can make a whole Christian." -A.W. Tozer (Of God and Men)

"We do not start our Christian lives by working out our faith for ourselves; it is mediated to us by Christian tradition, in the form of sermons, books and established patterns of church life and fellowship. We read our Bibles in the light of what we have learned from these sources; we approach Scripture with minds already formed by the mass of accepted opinions and viewpoints with which we have come into contact, in both the Church and the world. . . . It is easy to be unaware that it has happened; it is hard even to begin to realize how profoundly tradition in this sense has moulded us." – J.I. Packer (Fundamentalism and the Word of God)

–
–
–
–
–
–
–
–
–
–
–
–

LETTER ONE

To my dear Earnest,

"The end is coming, . . . but . . . don't worry too much. It'll take a while." Such is the hidden sentiment behind the pious words spilling from the lips of pastors, priests, seminarians, and pew-sitting-church-dwellers in our land – the land of Ignorantia. Never dreaming of uttering such an obvious and self-condemning laziness, these Ignorantians deceive themselves. There is a deep urgency to know the Holy Scriptures intimately, but the citizens of our prosperous nation have unwittingly procrastinated. They have become convinced that they are each Bible scholars of the highest ilk, and this has led to no small Ignorantian tragedy. Religious consumers, they are. They read fictional stories about the end times, and thus believe they know the Word of God. Because they are ecstatically moved by musical incantations, Ignorantians think they can expound on the sacred text's teaching of proper worship. They read four-hundred-year-old theologians instead of the thousands year old pages of the divine. No! Worse. They read what a modern Ignorantian has written about what a four-hundred-year-old theologian has said. "Now," they declare, without having dissected the apostle, "I understand Paul." Who could have imagined such a state of affairs? Christendom in Ignorantia has produced publishing houses, conference circuits, recording artists, and films, all orbiting its most powerful resource – the Scripture itself. Yet, in spite of all the commercial products sold under the Bible-banner, the Ignorantians are ignorant of what the Scriptures actually say.

I felt it necessary to write to you, my dear friend, to prepare you for your mission field. It is not what you would imagine. You're blessed to have had missionary parents who could raise you in the far away Tribe of Verum. If I understand your previous correspondence rightly, the entire village has come to believe on Christ. Their only book is the Bible. It is read daily. Verumian knowledge has increased rapidly thanks to daily focus on the inspired words. Transformative is too soft a term. Now, listen to me young man! The Ignorantians are very different from the Verumians. Your parents have done right by you. Your Verumian upbringing has insulated you from the beguiling diversions of this land . . . my land. When you arrive here, you must be on guard. Christendom will devour you. Crosses and steeples abound. Platitudinous and syrupy words drip from the lips of the Ignorantian churchmen. Bright lights, stages, and slogans can seduce even the faithful.

My singular goal in writing to you, young Earnest, is to demand that you do one thing. As you move about in Ignorantia, while you observe the sermons of Ignorantian preachers, and listen to Ignorantian music, that you keep one Verumian directive always in mind – to know the Bible as completely as you may, and to urge Ignorantians to follow you in this discipline. You see, Earnest, you are coming here to reach men for the Savior. That should always be your principle mission. But . . . there is a very difficult task which is especially needed in our land. Once men are saved they must become students of the Word. This is a different sort of conversion. Rather than salvation, I describe the metamorphosis of an Ignorantian into a Verumian. I'm talking about the renewal of the Christian mind. Henceforth, I will refer to this change from laziness and apathy to faithfulness and study as "mental migration." It is a migration from nescience to cognizance – from aimlessness to fulfillment.

My words will be long, for letters, but in the pages that follow I will be seeking to provide a handbook of sorts for understanding the Christian mind, as it exists in your new mission field. This handbook will be the culmination of my continuing correspondence to you. I've tried for years to gain a hearing among my countrymen – to shake them from their delusion. In these writings, I will explain how it is that an entire nation has come to believe they know a book they seldom read. If you give me a fair hearing, Earnest, you'll not only avoid the temptation to become an Ignorantian, but perhaps also gain some insight in helping them embrace the ways of your beloved Verumians too.

Few will listen. For those who do, you'll find yourself at a loss for the right words. You and I have a love for the Bible that far outpaces mere infatuation. We are obsessed! It is the frustration of our variety of men that we are never quite able to verbally capture the urgency, weight, majesty, joy, and benefit of that obsession. Our listeners' blank nods of passionless agreement reveal that they just . . . don't get it. If we try to tell them so, directly, they feel insulted and call us arrogant. They'll tear Scripture about judgmentalism out of context and use it against us. Those are some of the few verses they always seem to know. I tell you, the modern Ignorantian mind is quite clever. Its defenses are strong.

You may share our letters with whomever you wish. Perhaps these pages will be helpful. I've no business writing a book. Even if I did feel so compelled, no Ignorantian would likely read it. No other Verumian would ever have the need. But maybe . . . just maybe . . . you'll find some stranger who longs for instruction. Perhaps some citizen of my misguided nation will be, hereby, convinced of the eternal value of the Scriptures. Nevertheless, these words are not for the faint hearted. These are hard truths, Earnest. With that, let us focus on the Christian mind!

Grids

How does one become convinced that he is a scholar of a book he seldom reads? Perhaps you will notice this strange phenomenon wherein, even those who admit an ignorance of the Scriptures, feel themselves qualified to tell others what they mean. They choose careers, marry, raise children, and vote unto major world impact on the basis of their understandings of a book they do not know. Academically-minded Christian Ignorantians think they know it to a great depth. Indeed, they take pride in this supposed fact. The untrained ones carry a humility about their knowledge, but still sustain the belief that they've garnered enough of it through general overview that they may, justly, carry the strongest of opinions. This is an odd thing, to say the least. I suppose the problem with being deceived is that the man who is deceived does not know he is deceived . . . otherwise, he would not be deceived to begin with.

Moreover, the deception is so entrenched that if it were not so serious it would cause a thousand belly laughs. I have, on many occasions, observed two opposing Christian Ignorantians stand on stage at an institution of higher education and academically debate some alleged scriptural teaching. Each of them is undeniably convinced that he understands with exactness what the text is saying. Only, each of them has cobbled together five or so verses, disconnected from context, and buried under the words of other Ignorantians who do the same. To the untrained eye, they appear to be intellectual champions of the holy pages. To him who has understanding, they appear to be little more than talking groundhogs debating the weather on the basis of their own shadows. If you think me cruel for these words, please understand, I know this because . . . I've been the groundhog.

The lay-men and lay-women behave in a slightly more mystical way. They sit in circles and read one of about twenty or so well-known verses before posing the question, "Now what does that mean . . . to you?" Who would do such a thing with the pages of a medical journal, or a construction blueprint? What I want to impress upon you, my friend, is that the Bible makes an appearance in each case. For that reason, those involved believe that they are teaching or learning the Bible. What lies at the bottom of this confusion are different types of grids.

Grids are patterns of understanding. They guide interpretation, doctrinal perspectives, and general belief. Each denomination of Christianity has its own larger grid. If members read the Bible, they read it with that grid in mind. Sermons are prepared and heard through that grid. Are members learning the Bible? In a manner of speaking, they are. They are learning the Bible as it is presented by the grid. Further, each local congregation within a given denomination will likely have its own refined version of the larger denominational grid. This grid will be informed and molded by the preacher's own grid, as well as the grids brought to the local church by the individual members. It is for this reason, you will discover, that two local bodies of the same denomination, with very similar grids, will have very different views on a particular doctrinal issue. The grids are similar because they are both passed down from the parent denominational pattern, but the difference reveals that the combination of various grids does result in a few variations here or there. This alone is somewhat unavoidable and not entirely destructive, but it gets worse.

The grid is supported by passages of Scripture. In small-groups, summer children's camps, and sermons, these verses are presented. Better yet, a few short verses that seem particularly memorable are offered for memorization. These few biblical sentences are all most Christian Ignorantians will ever learn. They were chosen because they support the grid. And thus begins the lifelong belief that the individual knows the Bible, when what he really knows is a particular grid. Still, we shouldn't be too hard on the church leaders yet. There's nothing wrong with the practice described, so long as the learner truly begins to study the Scriptures broadly, and challenge presuppositions. This rarely happens.

Whatever the denominational leaders had in mind, most of the members give up learning the Bible, but continue learning the grid. After all, they have to make decisions in life. The grid, and its proponents, provides some guidance in making those decisions. Plus, the grid seems easier to learn than the vast literary body of Scripture. Beyond this, people have opinions. In our nation, everyone's opinion is supposed to be equally valid. Therefore, discussions are often based on the grid, but seldom is a verse of Scripture mentioned. Christian Ignorantians will often say things like, "The Bible says . . ." with no knowledge of exactly where in the Bible a particular concept is supposedly taught. A few years ago, I actually had a young couple demand with absolute certainty that the Bible somewhere says, "All sins are created equal." That concept, in truth, was more grid material than Bible material.

Now I don't want to depress you, dear Earnest, or drone on too long, but it does actually grow worse still. Because a particular character has memorized a few brief passages from the Bible, and absorbed a vast amount of theological gridding, he may decide that he knows the Bible better than most. Then, with the best of intentions, he determines to go to Bible

College. What more noble a notion could there be for one who wishes to know . . . the Bible? Yes, he must go to Bible College, but which one? How should he choose? Well, he must consult . . . the grid. Almost universally, such young adventurers will choose an institution of higher theological education that closely follows the grid with which they were raised. There they will begin learning to refine the grid even more. Now you might suppose that surely in Bible College, the Bible will be finally and fairly studied. If so, you're not entirely wrong.

Bible College will present alternative grids to the student. He will see why other denominations and other congregations have different grids than the one with which he was raised. This will involve an examination of various proof-texts for the doctrinal positions of the grids. On occasion, a course will be taken that focuses specifically on a book of the Bible. Finally! However, these are typically overview courses in which the general grid, held by the college, will be expounded and defended. It will then be reinforced by the other students. Our specimen becomes a master of grids, discussing and diagramming them with scientific precision. He will ultimately gain a PhD. Sadly, this may merely be a PhD in grids. He will then become a pastor, professor, or author. He'll teach the grid to his hearers, just as others taught it to him during his youth. The cycle will begin again.

This is one of the central reasons, dear Earnest, that Christian Ignorantians dwelling in ivory towers believe they have become experts in biblical study even though they know very little real Bible.

You might be wondering at this point, what examples I may have of this sort of gridding. Well, I have no shortage of illustrations. Yet, to demonstrate the point, I'll address a few.

In Matthew 7:21, Jesus warns,

> *"Not everyone who says to Me, 'Lord, Lord,' will enter the kingdom of heaven, but he who does the will of My Father who is in heaven will enter. Many will say to Me on that day, 'Lord, Lord, did we not prophesy in Your name, and in Your name cast out demons, and in Your name perform many miracles?' And then I will declare to them, 'I never knew you; depart from Me, you who practice lawlessness.' "Therefore everyone who hears these words of Mine and acts on them, may be compared to a wise man who built his house on the rock. And the rain fell, and the floods came, and the winds blew and slammed against that house; and yet it did not fall, for it had been founded on the rock. Everyone who hears these words of Mine and does not act on them, will be like a foolish man who built his house on the sand. The rain fell, and the floods came, and the winds blew and slammed against that house; and it fell—and great was its fall."*

These words, from our Savior, demand reverence and a healthy sense of fear. No man desires the horror of hearing the Lord pronounce, "I never knew you." No man wishes to be in the house destroyed by wind and flood. I'm sure for you, and your Verumian countrymen, this passage sobers the Christian mind for disciplined obedience. Not so for many a Christian Ignorantian. They water it down like the foolish man's flooded house.

First, the discussion of houses is usually reserved for Sunday school sing-a-longs. There's a catchy little tune the children all learn. For this reason, when they approach this section of Scripture, they read over it thinking they already know the point. But wait! The houses are not window-dressing. The tale of these houses is not disconnected from the previous verses. We are still reading about the horrifying fate of certain men. These houses illustrate a point about the characters who will say, "Lord, Lord," in hopeless desperation. Now, Earnest, we'll come back to those houses in a moment. For now, let's consider the situation of our hopeless fellows from verses twenty-two and twenty-three.

To hear the Ignorantian preach about these men is usually quite a different experience than reading the page. The truth of the matter is typically incompatible with their grids. Ignorantian ministers often give the impression, whether intended or not, that little more than mental assent is necessary for the second birth. After reading this bit from the text, they'll say something like, "Here we find the sorts of lost souls who only appear in our midst on Easter and Christmas. There are a great number like them in our nation today. They claim to be Christians, but don't truly practice their faith." This fits the grid nicely. This particular grid might hold that so long as citizens recite a prayer, or regularly attend church, they can rest assured that they have been granted salvation. Upon hearing the pastor's words, the members of the local congregation can conclude that they are unlike the fellows in the text. They attend church some bit more than twice a year. They practice their faith. They have no reason to fear God. The grid rocks them, as if in a cradle, into a complacent slumber.

You, dear Earnest, know better. I need not even mention that the characters our Lord describes are far from the nominal figures presented by Ignorantian pastors. How could it ever be said that they are like modern men who only appear twice per year? Conversely, anyone about whom it could be said that they, "prophesied, cast out demons, and performed miracles" in Jesus' name, would appear to the highest of churchmen to be "on fire" in their service. You do not need me to point out that Jesus nowhere denies that his hypothetical figures engaged in such actions. Rather, in spite of these wondrous works, they are doomed. Nominal citizens of Christendom, they are not. To the rest of us, they would appear to have maintained the utmost devotion. Now, let's return to this issue of different kinds of houses.

Houses are serious investments, Earnest. Like a house, a man's life is a great investment, indeed. Each moment of life we make choices to obey the Lord or not; to hear his words and act on them – or not. Each decision, therefore, is like making a contribution to that larger investment. The question is, "Am I investing in the right kind of house, or the wrong kind of house?" At the end of our lives, Earnest, we can assess what has been done and consider whether we made a good investment or not. The desperate gents crying "Lord, Lord," may have added a fine patio onto their house, but it was a house on sand, nonetheless. That, dear boy, is the teaching of the text. I know, I know . . . your Verumian upbringing has already taught you this. After all, one needs only to read the words on the page to see it.

Nevertheless, an Ignorantian would ask me, "But what does that do to this doctrine or that doctrine?" These are fair questions. Notice, though, that these questions are about grids, and not about the passage. Notice, also, that the implication of the question is that the meaning of the text should be decided upon by the grid, and not the other way 'round.

Young man, you should also be warned that at times the grid supplies information that is nowhere taught, directly or indirectly, in Scripture. Ignorantians prefer straight lines and seamless categories. Imagine an assortment of lines that seem to roughly imply the shape of a triangle.

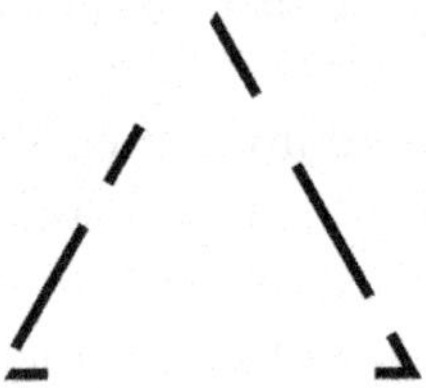

We might well assume, and our minds will suggest, that the image we are seeing is obvious. Now since we have a great number of other shapes to determine, we might simply fill in the lines, and move on. From that point forward, the simple triangle will become doctrine. No one sees a very good reason to deny the clear implication. The triangle gets preached. Hymns about the triangle are written, and it is taken for granted that anyone who denies the triangle doctrine is but a fool . . . or . . . a false teacher of foreign angles. But the decision was hastily made. It was assumed that where the shape was silent, that is to say pieces were missing, one should draw the line that springs most easily to mind. Nevertheless, in this case the doctrine of the triangle was wrong. In fact, it should be shaped as an arrow.

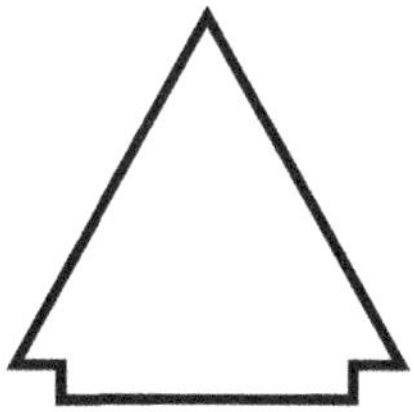

Now you're likely wondering, Earnest, what in the world is this old tinkerer on about? Just wait and see.

Ignorantian grids must make sense of the Bible in a way that is coherent. There is nothing incoherent about the triangle, thus it makes a fine . . . albeit incorrect grid. Take, for example, the common belief that when an individual becomes a Christian his name is added to the Lamb's book of life. Just as the mind assumes the shape of the incomplete triangle, the Christian mind assumes the shape of the doctrine. I imagine this conclusion was drawn just as hastily. As with what we've been calling, the doctrine of the triangle, the belief that names are added to a book has been preached, hymns have been written, and anyone who challenges the notion is a fool or worse. Yet, the Word of God nowhere says any such thing. Not one place in the whole of the sacred text references names being added to the book! Nowhere! Yet, Christian Ignorantians strongly believe that the Bible plainly says so. It does not. Yet again, we have an example of the Ignorantian belief that they know the text when, in reality, they know the grid. This time we see that the conclusions are drawn not from a misunderstanding of what is said, but from what is not said.

I don't want to belabor the point, my friend, but I should say that this gridding is not only changed by academic theological gridworkers, but also popular level folk theology. Thereby, the grid is molded over sentimental ideas from what are called "Christian living" publications. Consider the standard Ignorantian statement, "Prayer is a two-way conversation." The idea sounds nice, but it is more gridical than biblical.

Nowhere, in the sacred Scriptures, is it ever suggested that prayer should be a two-way conversation. As you well know, Earnest, prayer happens when we make our requests known to God. Jesus taught his disciples this in Matthew 6:9-13. Moreover, in Philippians 4:6, Paul flatly defines it as, "making your requests known to God." Nevertheless, in our land, the people in the pews have been told that they are not engaged in prayer unless they are talking to, and hearing from, God. You can imagine how that's received. Since most believers don't "hear" from God every time they pray, they tend to mope about worrying that they've angered the Divine. "Why do others always hear from God in these two-way conversations, but I do not?" This confusion has to be remedied, so the Ignorantian penitent listens to the silence of his solitude with shifting eyes and expectant heart. Nothing. After several days of nothing, he convinces himself that a particular thought might be . . . yes. One notion seems particularly profound or wise. Enough so, that the sad fellow decides this barely noticed flutter must be the voice of the Almighty. "Perhaps," he thinks, "this is what they mean when they say the voice will be still and small." No check is made as to the scriptural authenticity of the arbitrary idea that wondered across the Ignorantian mind. It is, after all, a word directly from the King's lips to the servant's ear. Why should he question it? And there you have it, Earnest. The Ignorantian does not even realize he has just convinced himself of some private revelation. This, as you and I know, is how cults are born.

Sometimes the self-deception is subtler. Sometimes the Bible makes a brief appearance. You see, some Christian Ignorantians are perceptive enough to know that the Scriptures consist of the Word of God. They surmise that if this two-way conversation is to take place it might be that God's part in the whole matter might mystically arise from the text. Yet, they can't be bothered with careful study to learn the mind of God on particular topics, then apply biblical wisdom to specific situations. Instead, they open the Bible and begin reading. The only difference between this specimen and the fellow listening to his own thoughts is that our new example lets the words on the page pass before his eyes as he . . . listens to his own thoughts. He, likewise, catches a notion that has more to do with some film he recently viewed than with the text. Subjectively, he decides this notion is somehow the meaning of the words just read . . . at least that's their meaning . . . for him. Again, notice that this man will likely rise from his knees believing he understands, better than most, what the Bible says. This is how new grids begin. This is also how cults that twist the Scripture are born.

Yet the teaching that prayer must be a two-way conversation will never be found in the pages of God's Word. It simply isn't there. However, it is a part of many Ignorantian grids, all the same. And thus, we now see that the focus on these grids can affect major theological constructs and practical Christian living.

At this moment, faithful Earnest, I imagine your chin is on the floor. Doubt me if you like, but you'll see it all when you arrive in Ignorantia. You'll find my words are, in fact, far too soft. It's worse than you think. The grid even affects the means by which our ceremonial worship services are conducted. Because of the traditions from which different sorts of worship services arise, there is a deeply entrenched motivation to protect and defend them. The assumption that worship services should be done in exactly the manner a particular Ignorantian believes they should, informs the grid. Sifting the Bible with the grid in hand, denominational leaders search for evidence to support a given method, style, or type of weekly gathering. Take, for example, the question of whether music should be involved at all.

It is a dying tradition, thank the Lord, but some Christian Ignorantians insist that instrumental music should have no part in such services. This likely dumbfounds you, my dear boy, for you are keenly aware that king David instituted elaborate musical worship, which absolutely involved instrumentation. No one needs to remind you, or your Verumian compatriots, that Paul instructed the Colossians to sing Psalms. Nor, Earnest, do you require the explanation that the very word "psalm" refers to music produced from stringed instruments. Nevertheless, there is a shrinking number in our land who have, for decades, demanded that such should not be done. On what do they base such an assertion? The Bible, of course . . . or . . . I should say, the Bible as it is presented by the grid. A given grid might reveal all sorts of things that no one, especially the human author, ever noticed.

Have you ever heard of the biblical character Jubal, from the book of Genesis? In chapter four, verse twenty-one, Moses tells us that, "He was the father of all those who play the lyre and pipe." Did you know that this Jubal was in the family line of Cain, the same who killed his brother Abel? It is, therefore, reasoned that because Cain committed an evil act, his entire progeny must be wicked in precisely the same manner as he. Since Jubal is in this line, and since Jubal was the father of lyre and pipe players, and since the lyre and the pipe are musical instruments . . . musical instruments must be evil. They're not too evil for enjoyment, but these particular Ignorantians seem to think this means they're too evil for use in the church. Now, no self-respecting Verumian would have ever come to such an absurd conclusion. Ignorantians, though, conclude all sorts of nonsense. This is accomplished by valuing most, a particular grid. Long live the grid! The grid must be defended at all cost! With such a vacuous commitment, the biblical authors must be forced into submission. They must be enslaved to the service of the grid. It matters little that the Bible nowhere teaches that all of Cain's decedents must be villainous because of his fratricide. Look for yourself, Earnest. The worst of his offspring, one Lamech, did likewise kill. Yet, his killing may well have been self-defense. Furthermore, even if they were all tyrants of the highest order, why should their inventions be spurned? Ridiculous!

Understand, my Verumian friend, that this issue is so minor that most Ignorantians are unaware of it. It is, as I said, a dying perspective. I mention it not because of its prevalence, but because of how well it illustrates the impact of grid-dependence on Ignorantian worship. No less incongruous thinking goes into Ignorantian wars over styles of music. Those who use instruments debate endlessly the sort of music God must prefer. Expectedly, each supposes God most delights in the genre that strikes his own fancy. The same is true of the order of the service, the use of church creeds, the frequency of communion, attire to be worn, and organizational culture. Each denomination has a tradition, and most must admit the pressing of the text into the grid with respect to at least some of these items.

Forgive me, my companion, for I've likely gone too far. I did not mean to do violence to the very concept of grids. We all have them. Grids are inescapable. We may no sooner read the words on the page and begin to organize our thoughts, then a grid will emerge. And, without being too platonic in my illustration, there must be a perfect grid. If the Word is without contradiction, then there is a perfect understanding of it. There must exist, if only in the mind of God, a grid which makes sense of all biblical teaching – one that is consistent with reality. A perfect systematic theology. I'll refer to this higher scheme as The Great Verumian Grid, not because you Verumians perfectly know the mind of God, but because you are the closest of all.

It is common enough to hear Ignorantians claim, "I care not for a theological system. I believe the Bible!" The temptation to roll the eyes is difficult to resist. For all the piety and glory-lauding, such a fellow has merely scratched away the name of some famed theologian from the top of his grid. He has removed its manufacturer's label and etched the term "biblical" in its place. The Great Verumian Grid is not found by mixing and matching.

Take a boy who is being taught mathematics. He has been shown how to add two-digit numbers together. The problem before him is thirty-seven plus forty-two. What his instructor has in mind is that the child will learn how to let the answer arise naturally from the numerical inputs. This will lead him to the proper conclusion – seventy-nine. But, what if he decides to give up on the proper application of addition he has been taught? What if a fellow student passes him a piece of paper on which are scribbled three possible answers? Imagine further that the lad begins focusing more on the suggested answers than on the problem itself. He reasons that greater minds than his have likely come up with these possibilities. He happens to know that his closest friend supplied the answer sixty-seven. Because of his great respect for this particular classmate, he begins to favor this answer. Another answer is eighty-eight. The little fellow has noticed that many of the answers he's seen in the class seem to have eights in them. Thus, his presupposition leads him toward this answer. A third answer, seventy-six, has been circled and starred. This indicates that seventy-six is the most popular choice. Unfortunately, all guesses are wrong.

I'll not remain mysterious about this, Earnest. The addition problem represents the Bible, or some particularly difficult passage. The suggested answers represent varying theological conclusions to which theologians have arrived. Sixty-seven, the answer provided by the close friend, represents the boy's tradition. Eighty-eight represents his presuppositions about reality, based on his past experience. The third answer, seventy-six, stands for the most popular theological positions in the larger cultural sphere. Our little friend starts with possible answers, picks one, and then attempts to impose it onto the problem. Backwards! Ignorantians, similarly, begin with theological answers that either come from traditions, presuppositions, or popular opinions. Those are then forced onto the text. The Verumian way, as you and I know, is to begin with the problem and let it reveal the answer last. In brief, start with the Bible . . . discover the grid. Never, start with the grid! This, I know you'd agree, is how to begin constructing . . . nay . . . discovering, The Great Verumian Grid.

Now let's consider this from another angle. Suppose the boy is handed, but ignores the answers from his classmates at first. Instead, he devotes himself to answering the problem properly. He has seen, and cannot forget, the potential solutions written down on the page. Nevertheless, he works out the solution on his own. Once satisfied, he may then reflect on the previously delivered answers of tradition, presupposition, and consensus. In the case of our analogy, those sources delivered only wrong options. However, we might imagine a similar scenario in which the popular opinion was correct, or the one based on tradition, or the one based on his own presuppositions. The lad would not be unwise to compare his own answer with the solutions offered by others. This could bring great confirmation to his mind. Conversely, he might educate his classmate . . . a novel idea. What he must not do, my compatriot, is to assume that because a particular source happened to be correct about this particular problem, that they should henceforth, be assumed correct regarding all math problems. In like manner, we may consider whether a particular grid matches what we have discovered from the text, but we should always begin with the text.

Grids can be helpful, though. Surprised? Well, they can. If a given individual studies the Scriptures and arrives at a solution about, say, the nature of Christ, which is completely at odds with almost all competing Christian grids, this fact can serve as a warning sign. Think of the reasonable conclusion our schoolboy might draw if he worked out the answer twenty-seven, and all but two other classmates answered seventy-nine. This should give him pause.

And with that, my young correspondent, I've said all I care to say about this business of gridding. Like I previously mentioned, you'll see it all when you arrive on these Ignorantian shores. In my next message to you, I hope to write about the problem of cultures. You'll be hearing from me soon!

Your friend and informant,
Solomon

LETTER TWO
On Cultures

To my dear Earnest,

Smoking a pipe is fine, but cigarettes are a stench in the nostrils of God. Well . . . it's all yellow fingertips to me, but they can scuffle about it if they like. Shaking hands at church is a must, but greeting one another with a holy kiss will put you on the fast track to fornication and the Apostle Paul can just deal with it. You may do as you please with your cash, just so long as you give ten percent to the Master, after all, isn't that how the New Testament reads?

I've got news for you, Earnest, the lack of study and dependence on grids has led us to a further problem in our land. Cultures are developed in the Ignorantian churches that provide the essence of the grids as they relate to moral living. Each denomination, and at a lower level, each congregation has its own cultural norms relating to the living out of the Christian faith. This results in a minor cosmos of some version of Christianity that newcomers may explore. These little worlds then serve as visible tutors for all members. It's so subtle, in fact, that most newcomers never notice it. They just . . . sort of . . . fall in line.

You'll find, my friend, that some Ignorantian congregations find it perfectly acceptable to use, what in my day was called, common language. By this, I mean profanity. It is, in fact, a rising trend. It's defended as a manifestation of a genuine, and unhypocritical heart. "We need to be real!" some will say. Conversely, in other congregations, there is such an emphasis placed upon this matter that ministers self-consciously trade out perfectly regular biblical terms like "ass" or "pisseth" because despite the proper context, these words result in a fair amount of squeamishness.

Or, consider the question of elementary education. You've likely heard that we have an expansive, yet thoroughly Ignorantian school system, run by the government. For some congregations, tis a grave sin to allow children to enroll in Caesar's classroom. In others, it is taught that homeschooling, or private school education is unpatriotic, and the former is even dangerous for social development. Oh dear. As I wrote those last four words, I gagged and came near to vomit upon myself.

Human sexuality has its own culturally communicated norms. One church will say that it's fine for young romancers to kiss as they like, so long as it's above the neck. Others say, youngsters may hold hands and no more. Still, more congregations demand that no touching of the opposite sex should ever be permitted outside of marriage. As for the married folk, most congregations quietly hold that once in the marriage bed, nothing is forbidden. However, some try to send the message that certain "debased" acts should still be avoided.

Some congregations are fine with divorced clergy, while others call it anathema. Some say you may drink beverage alcohol while others declare it the devil's elixir. Some consider what they call "senior pastors" to wield ultimate authority, while others grant rule to deacons, or the members themselves. Some imply that a particular political party is acceptable, while others demand that we have no part in politics. And when it comes to entertainment, there is a genuine spectrum. Churches range from giving the impression that believers should avoid almost all of it, to implying that . . . anything goes.

Some of these items are directly communicated from the pulpit, but what I want you to know, before you get here, is much more dangerous. It almost always goes unnoticed. For the most part, these ideas are quietly communicated by the church culture into which the newcomer enters. As the convert looks around his new Christian cosmos, and begins to wear its clothes, he unconsciously accepts, "This is what Christianity is like. These beliefs represent the Christian mind. If I act as they act, and believe what they believe, I'll be living out the Christian faith." Yet, the new convert may never bother to consult the Bible to discover answers to these important questions.

After all, despite what the church may say, the culture vividly communicates to him that studying the Bible can best be done with culture-rich, culture-approved, devotional publications. The Christian toddler functions as toddlers always do. Small children do not read massive home economics texts in order to learn the proper means by which they may successfully serve the goals of house and community. They watch their own families! They imitate their parents and siblings! They repeat what they hear others say, and when they repeat words that represent a culture foreign to the home (for instance a common word) they are disciplined. No less occurs in the church. The new convert follows the crowd, and if he ever echoes the thoughts of another culture, a signal is sent through the shifting of eyes.

Cultures, dear Earnest, emerge when a group experiences some tragedy, or seeks to accomplish some goal. Usually the early days of that new culture are defined by stressful experiences shared by founding members. When those anxieties are alleviated by some successful strategy, rule, philosophy or practice, the answer becomes a norm and is relied upon by the culture going forward. The most common anxiety is the need for a leader. This is simply demonstrated by separating twenty people into four groups of five. Tell any one of those groups that there are no set rules and they are to decide for themselves what the group will be about. Everyone will instantly grow anxious. The reason for the silent mental suffering is that no one will know precisely what they are meant to be doing. Each member wants someone to lead. They crave direction. If a leader emerges, and provides purpose, rules and organization, he will have assuaged the group's existential crisis. The strategies, rules, or philosophies he used to satisfy those initial anxieties will become normative. He has begun to craft the culture. This happens despite the larger denominational influence or lack thereof. The early days of the culture soon become part of the culture's history and legend. Those who did not experience it dare not criticize this sacred past . . . at least . . . not if they want to remain part of the new culture. Identity has been defined, and will be further defined as the Ignorantian culture ages and faces new problems.

For instance, take the Ignorantian church culture regarding the use of the gift of tongues. A new convert wanders into his new group and notices that during worship a number of individuals seem to spontaneously vocalize emotional outbursts in a worshipful expression. Nobody seems to know what any particular individual is on about. It's daftly distracting, and our toddler-man will notice a few shifty initiates struggling to work out whether and how they should make their own attempts. No one can translate it, and no one tries. I tell you the truth, Earnest, for I could not fabricate it. It's the oddest spectacle. Given enough time, and social pressure, the toddler-man will either abandon the culture, or join in the ecstatic fun. Now, you and I know that ambiguity persists regarding the nature of tongues, and even granting the charismatic expression, Paul calls out the manifestation just described in 1 Corinthians 14.

I've known many godly men and women who conform to a subtler model who would likewise reject the unfettered congregational rabble-static of the Ignorantians previously noted. I'm not slagging off the whole ordeal, though you know I have my doubts. Rather, I'm calling out the phenomenon adopted by the copycat convert who never consults the pages of the text, but in an infantile manner, simply accepts what he sees around him.

Perhaps, instead, I should have begun with a rather benign cultural suggestion that is ever-present in Ignorantian Christian groups today. Namely, I'm on about the emergence of the accountability partner. Three decades ago a few well-known Ignorantian clergymen were found out for their moral improprieties. One was a television preacher who was caught with a prostitute. A few were guilty of financial misconduct. Shameful! Nonetheless, Ignorantians began to scramble. What must we do to stop it? In many church cultures the solution came with the notion that everyone needs a partner. Each man needs his own gatekeeper, as it were. Each woman needs the same. They could keep eyes on one another, and ensure adherence to whatever moral code the particular culture preferred.

It wasn't too long before each new convert was assigned or recommended such a companion at the day of conversion. They were to speak regularly to one another, discuss habits, and pray together. These, by the way, are all beneficial practices that should be carrying on among believers anyway. Yet, the idea was that such relationships would serve to prevent scandal.

Honestly, this didn't sound like a bad idea. In truth, young Earnest, I don't necessarily object. Instead, I'm trying to drive at the development of such cultural artifacts as these. The primary problem with accountability partners is that they're easy to trick. Partner A needs only to lie to Partner B after committing sinful offense X. Even with the best intentions, Partner A may think, "I know that shouldn't have happened, and I should tell B about it, but I can get over this one myself. He doesn't need to know about this particular issue. After all, he hasn't reported any shortcomings in a while. I don't want to be the first." Once this rationalization is made, and the accompanying anxiety is assuaged, an unconscious norm will have been established. If A so chooses, he may not always faithfully report his sins in the future. This effectively negates the use of the whole enterprise. "But what if both partners are faithful and honest?" If that were the case, then a partner would not be required from the start.

No matter how advanced the partnership becomes, there are always workarounds. Recently these crafty Ignorantians invented a computer program that would report to Person B all the websites visited by Person A. Yet, it requires less craftiness to bypass such a technology, say, by using a different device, than it took for its creation. If a man wants to sin without his partner knowing it, there is little inhibiting the act. Nevertheless, the need for an accountability partner has almost reached the level of creedal authority in many Ignorantian congregations. If only the toddler-man would deeply begin studying the scriptures he would find a more reliable compass.

It brings to mind the life of young Joseph in Genesis 39:6-9. The Bible reads,

> *Now Joseph was handsome in form and appearance. It came about after these events that his master's wife looked with desire at Joseph, and she said, "Lie with me." But he refused and said to his master's wife, "Behold, with me here, my master does not concern himself with anything in the house, and he has put all that he owns in my charge. There is no one greater in this house than I, and he has withheld nothing from me except you, because you are his wife. How then could I do this great evil and sin against God?"*

Now, you already know this, young missionary, but the surprising thing at play here passes the Ignorantian eyes so swiftly that they never see it. Expressing his deep appreciation for all the ways his master had been good to him, and all the things his master had given him, we expect the final line to read, "How then could I do this great evil and sin against my master, Potiphar?" Alas, he serves a higher Master! Young Joseph, full of hormones, far from any other believer, much less an accountability partner, refrains from sexual gratification. He does not refrain because of a commitment to his master, benevolent as he has been. He forgoes the act because of God! God is Joseph's accountability partner! God is the reason to stay pure! Had it merely been a matter of offending his earthly master, our hero could have easily rationalized, "Am I not to do as my master's wife says?" Or perhaps he would reason, "She likely operated this way with previous servants." Moreover, if it were only concern for Potiphar's feelings, he could convince himself, "Potiphar will never know, and thus, will be no worse for it." Imagine further the possibility that Potiphar, dealing in the position so close to the king, may have been a eunuch. If so, he may not even care about the indiscretion. There are always means to rationalize offenses against men, just as there are excuses to deceive an accountability partner . . . just . . . this . . . once. The Verumian principle is, "be accountable to God." If, like Joseph, a man is ultimately focused on divine appreciation, all dark self-deceptions dissolve around his matchless light.

Now, the cultural device known as the accountability partner has some merit as long as the higher goal is accountability to the Master. Iron sharpens iron. We bear each other's burdens. Scripture demands the confessing of sins to one another, and this seems to have observable benefits for substance abusers. Yet, Christian Ignorantians legalistically treat the idea of an accountability partner as though it is an end in itself – a fail-safe against sinful activity. Culturebloat!

It gets worse, my friend, for one Ignorantian culture is designed, consciously or not, to insulate from other cultures. Once you've got the toddler-man, you have to keep him pacified. He must know that other cultures can't be trusted. Just as any toddler develops a taste for the homebrew, the toddler-man must be shown that milk from any other culture is tainted. Now this is an exceedingly fine point, Earnest, and many Ignorantians would miss it. There is dangerous milk out there. Worse! There is poison in deceptive cartons. Nonetheless, it is not always the case. Forgive my rambling. I'll get on with it now.

The choice milk in some Ignorantian groups is expository preaching. "Ah, of course," you say. Yes . . . of course indeed - If by expository preaching we mean the faithful Verumian explanation of what the Bible has to say, without distortion. Yet, and this will surprise you, Earnest, these Ignorantians teach in their griddical schools that this means only focusing on one small section of text at a time. Ignorantian preachers may reference other texts, but they dare not turn to them. They further mean to remove any illustration. Now, a process that sounds as though it has its merits is, of course, an examination of the text as it relates to some grid. The important thing to notice about this definition of expository preaching is that it is nowhere illustrated in the pages of the Bible. Biblical preachers used illustration, and they moved about in their Scriptures to make the point. No biblical sermon would be acceptable milk by these Ignorantian standards. Don't misunderstand, my boy. There is nothing particularly wrong with preaching by such guidelines. The danger is that congregants are taught to avoid alternative expositions. Preachers who use illustrations or jump around in the text to make a point, are uneducated, unreliable, cherry-picking, egotists. At least, that's what the Ignorantians say.

What I find striking, in the whole ordeal, is that Ignorantian Bible College students are so obviously inconsistent – or perhaps it is their professors. They will listen to a systematic theology lecture, which requires jumping around in the text, from a professor who is witty and full of amusing anecdotes, in order to learn a grid. They will praise the teacher's high intellect, and share his deep insights with friends.

However, when a country preacher delivers a sermon in which he connects the biblical teaching on, say, atonement by referencing a variety of passages from throughout God's Word and drives it home with an emotionally powerful story, they'll declare him an out-of-touch bumpkin. Lunacy! Inconsistency! Ignorantian!

This is a culturally developed, philosophy of preaching that is at once elitist and unnecessary. That said, Earnest, it's also perfectly fine. The text can be expounded upon splendidly using the Ignorantian definition, that is of course if it has The Great Verumian Grid in mind. The problem is that these culturebloaters act as though all other forms of preaching are subpar, and in saying so, they exclude many leather-lunged, anointed, Verumian expositors. Nevertheless, the cultural creation is used to prevent the toddler-man from drinking perfectly . . . good . . . milk.

That's all I have time to add, at present. I've need of adding more milk to my tea. I've switched brands lately, for though this dairy is not as flavorful, I've reason to believe it's purer and healthier. And just like that, I search for a minister and a culture that is focused on the purer, and thus healthier understanding of the pages of Scripture. It may not be the culture I enjoy the most, or prefer, but my preferences should be ever altered to conform to a higher culture, the culture of The Kingdom.

Your friend and informant,

Solomon

LETTER THREE
On Intuitions

To my dear Earnest,

My God would want my happiness, and my marriage is akin to being buried alive in a box made of charge-cards. He'd want me to divorce. Ignorantians covet their mirrors. Their Bibles are mirrors. Their churches are mirrors. Their God is a fantastic mirror. They do not see through glasses darkly. Ignorantians see clearest of all. But what they see is a clear reflection of themselves.

Young fellow, I've been stumbling over myself in a clumsy attempt to put my thoughts in order. How can I best express this problem of mirrors? If one could imagine that rather than words on paper, the words of Scripture were printed onto mirrors, one might get a sense of what I'm driving at. In this way, standing behind the written words is a reflection of the reader himself, complete with his own presuppositions, his own grid, his own culture, his own relationships, his own experiences, and the secularism of this age which has saturated the whole monstrosity. My imagery isn't even all that far off from the concrete physical reality. Now get this, young Earnest: Most Ignorantians carry around these small metal devices onto which is affixed a sheet of glass. Through it, they view their world. The reflective glass allows them to see images from their pasts, love letters electronically sent, pornographic encounters, and news items from an anti-Christian land. If they ever do read the Word of God, they read it through the same object used to view all earthly things, and the galaxies beyond. When one of them looks on the holy text as it appears on the glass, standing behind the words is a reflection of his own image. What a grand invention! What a marvelous feat! How fitting it is to serve as both a literal, and poetic example of the Ignorantian abuse of . . . intuition. To see this, we'll need to trade the mirror for a window, and I'll humbly make an attempt at its washing until it is transparently clear.

Intuition is a powerful device. We are prepackaged with it from birth. It must have come in with all the amniotic fluids or some such thing. Maybe not. It could be a feature of the immaterial soul. In any case, it is a gift from the Father. What it allows is the strong sense of a thing. It serves as a sort of internal evidence – this awareness of what is surely true. Yet, like most valuable tools, it gets distorted, bent, twisted, or in some other way mangled. During the course of life, and it can happen quite early, our experiences stress the intuition, as does our education, culture and relationships. And also like other tools, it needs to be recalibrated, adjusted, tweaked or . . . well, you get the idea. One would be right to ask how such a project could be accomplished. We need what we might call an intuition mold. Is there such a thing? Indeed.

To some degree, philosophy, science, logic, and historical inquiry can all help in the process of making adjustments to intuition. Poor stand-ins they are, though, for the greatest of all intuition molds. Namely, the Word of God. So depraved has man's intuition become that its current form does not match the teaching of the Bible. Because of this, certain passages strike the Ignorantian as shocking, surprising, relieving, and generally unexpected. This, of course, will not be true of you, my calibrated friend. Verum has produced in you the intuitions that match the written Word. What I must attempt now is the scrubbing of the pane. It's my job to ensure that when you arrive here, you understand how this business works. You see, a distorted intuition still functions, and still gets you to some truth, but what it loses, like any damaged tool, is accuracy.

Take the romantic and erotic for instance. What a beautiful interplay! Hold them in your mind, dear Earnest, while I pontificate on intuitions about God, for I will come back to them. Oh, and I hope I don't offend your youthful bashfulness. Little causes more excitement privately, and uneasiness publically, than the topic of sex. It will be key here in understanding the Ignorantian mind.

Since the vast majority of the history of the world has believed in some god or gods, it can hardly be too controversial to say that most humans intuit one. One famous man from the land of reformantia, once called it the sensus divinitatis – the sense of the divine. Now atheists will challenge the existence of such an intuition, but I'm not writing to you about them, now am I? We brothers should see the intuition of God as trivially acceptable. I know you'll agree. So for the consensus of man, that the reality of some god is a trusted intuition, creation has a clear purpose and function. Now enter human sexuality!

Goodness, satisfaction, pleasure, unity, longing, sacrifice, appreciation, and a subtle glimpse of the ontology of joy, are had in the throes of love! Intuitively, we know it! And even without yet experiencing it, Earnest, you know it from the internal longings you feel, and no doubt understand. Intuitively we know love is good. Our intuitions get us that far, and you Verumians, with your pristinely straightened faculties may go further. But almost every Ignorantian will agree with us on these matters. Love and sex are good. They are very, very good!

The history of this land has gotten much wrong, but has been mostly right on this matter, that is until the cultural intuition began to bend in the final third of the last century. It has continued to twist til this very day. Is it useless? Far from it. Is it accurate? No. Imagine with me, beloved brother, that we are standing on the surface of the moon. As moon-men, I ask you to point at the earth, only the size of an apple in our moon-men fields of vision. You point in the general direction as requested. Now, you're far more accurate than you could be. For instance, if you pointed opposite our home-world you'd be as wrong as can be imagined. Yet, from our distance, your pointing in earth's general direction may be off by only a few degrees, having the effect of general accuracy, but not precision. If we were to follow your line in some fantastic space vehicle, on our return trip, we'd flat miss the earth, and end up in some wild and distant realm. Perhaps we could call it, The Nearly Way Galaxy. What have we learned from our time as moon-men? We've learned that general accuracy is damning. We need precision.

Imprecise intuition allows my countrymen to point in the general direction of the truth about romance and eroticism. It's good! Naturally, there is great value in this marred intuition device they all have installed. Still, it's imprecision leads them past the ideal and into The Nearly Way Galaxy, and exponentially further from the truth than when they began.

As you have read in the pages of the Bible, men often seek to experience eroticism with multiple women. Women experience it with multiple men. Fortunately, most Christian Ignorantians still retain a correct enough intuition to be ashamed of such activities, though their intuitions that God would wish them happy despite their vows, is an inaccuracy leading to the mockery of the institution of marriage and the abuse of the institution of divorce. In this way, they pit their intuition against itself, and resolve the whole matter to their own satisfaction. At this stage I'll simply hope you haven't forgotten what I said about mirrors, for it's on full display here.

What you may be shocked to learn, my Verumian lad, is that what you saw denigrated in the first chapter of Paul's letter to the Romans, and the sixth chapter of the letter to the church at Corinth, commonly called First Corinthians, now meets the approval of many Christian Ignorantians. Namely, men experiencing eroticism with men, and women doing the same with women is now defended from the pages of the Holy Scriptures. I know, I know! Shocking! You'd be amazed how they torture the text until it coughs up what they want. The thing is, it all comes down to this blasted intuition problem.

Love is a good thing, as is eroticism. Ignorantians point to committed and monogamous erotic relationships between two men or two women, and see good things. This is because the intuitions about love, eroticism, and commitment are generally accurate, but not precisely so. You'll recall that I elucidated my thoughts about man's intuition of a Creator. Well, anyone can see what the Creator had in mind by simply observing the external physical structures of men and women. No, again, don't blush, Earnest. I'm telling you something dreadfully serious.

It's clear what this Creator purposed for sexuality. Combining the intuitions about the Creator with the intuitions about love and eroticism, a recalibrated and precise intuition will lead its user to the conclusion that men should fall in love with women and women with men. They should experience sexual pleasure together in an act of obedience and honor toward the Designer. This intuition should demonstrate that functioning in opposition to this is an act of disobedience to the Creator, and one's intuitions should lead in that direction even before reading a word of sacred text. Thus, precise intuitions do not land us in The Nearly Way Galaxy!

On this note, there is much more to say about distorted intuitions, and how they have resulted in churchmen and churchwomen calling one thing the other, and so on. I can't be too specific, dear friend, or the Ignorantian post office will not allow this letter to pass. Oh yes, it's gotten that bad, or at least I expect it will be soon. I hope this much will suffice to show that intuitions point in the general direction of something true, but without an intuition mold, like the Bible, they take one into a different world in which God never intended man. Now let's get back to the mirrors and round out the whole thing.

Here's a passage for us to use as a sample for our experiment:

> *For this reason God gave them over to degrading passions; for their women exchanged the natural function for that which is unnatural, and in the same way also the men abandoned the natural function of the woman and burned in their desire toward one another, men with men committing indecent acts and receiving in their own persons the due penalty of their error (*Romans *1:26,27).*

Now with this text in mind, my explanation should sing. When a Verumian reads it, he sees a clear instructive that matches his intuitions about anthropology and the physiology of both men and women. It perfectly parallels his intuitions about the Creator, and what the Creator clearly wants, as evidenced by the male and female designs. These items, in turn, are incredibly consistent with Verumian intuitions about love, eroticism, commitment and more.

But when an Ignorantian reads this text, he sees himself. He sees his culture. He sees harsh words that stand in opposition to his intuitions as stressed and bent by his personal experience and modern setting. They are words on a mirror, and his own reflection is as much a part of the meaning as the words. This means the text must be referring to something other than loving committed relationships. It must hint at pedophilia, rape, one-night-stands, or polyamory. It must mean this, because though the Ignorantian's intuition was generally right, it was bent under cultural and societal force. It didn't happen quickly, but over a lifetime. And now, though it still points to the general truth about the general topics, it misses the mark and sends the imprecise intuitor spinning through the universe.

Notice that I've used an example that is shocking to your Verumian eyes. I must be fair at this point and reveal that it is likewise shocking to some Christian Ignorantians whose intuitions are still formed enough. There are degrees of distortion, but it's distortion nonetheless. You'll recall I made some passing remarks about divorce, and we have to keep our Savior's caveats in mind, naturally. But Christian Ignorantians with straighter intuitions, make the same mistakes in other areas.

As previously illustrated, some violate the marriage covenant for unbiblical reasons because they intuit that their loving Creator Father would want them to be happy instead of faithful. When this occurs, not only does it also land one in The Nearly

Way Galaxy, but it serves as justification for the previously addressed crowd. "Surely loving, monogamous men with men is better than this day and night divorce of men and women." And though distorted intuitions can summon chaos in many areas of human sinfulness, the gargantuan knot of entangled-intuition that accompanies human sexuality serves as an obvious illustration.

The Bible is our great intuition mold. However, we have to remember our discussion of grids lest the intuition be molded to the grid rather than the Scriptures. We see this with controversial issues such as whether the Bible allows for a woman to serve as an elder. Ignorantians line up on both sides of that issue, and in most cases they have intuitions pressed, hardened, and shipped from some grid production company, rather than the biblical mold. When one allows the Bible to mold the intuition, it results in an intuitive device that is finely tuned. This is a useful thing, to be sure!

It may be used in life in general, but it is certainly helpful with theology, though most Ignorantian theologians slag it off. The finely tuned intuition allows the user to follow the truth of God's character as a just and loving Creator. This becomes important when one considers war and so-called slavery in the Old Testament. It helps see the truth of difficult doctrines like Hell and eternal judgement. It allows one to move about in the confusing waters of the nature of salvation, and navigate the question of who God will save. Now, most of this you already know, but what you might not expect is that those confused

Ignorantian theologians don't like this talk. I was once called to explain my position before a group of theology professors only to be mocked and told, "You can't trust your feelings!" In truth, they couldn't trust their own feelings about what my feelings would be, for though they meant to hurt my feelings, my feelings were not what they felt.

They mean well, but had they heard me out, they'd understand that I'm driving at studying Scripture enough that one gets a taste of the character of God. We come to know Him by molding our intuitions to his revealed text. What's the use of it, if I can't come to understand what He's like. Worst of all, the professors know better, though they don't know that they know.

Ask a question the Bible doesn't ask, and you'll get an answer the Bible doesn't give, but it neither means your answer is wrong, nor does it mean you can't know that it's right. In Ignorantia, politicians are arguing about how to regulate and legalize the use of an intoxicating plant-based substance. The theologians to whom I refer, are against it, and I think them correct. However, the Bible nowhere speaks to this substance. Moreover, these seminarians affirm the moderated use of alcoholic beverages. Is there a contradiction here? How does one make a conclusion in a matter not expressly discussed in the Word of God? It's not too terribly difficult.

One works from the material we do have, and relies on his intuition about God's character as it has been molded by the text. God would be opposed to the recreational use of the drug in question. Why? Because it damages the lungs and intoxicates the man. How do you know God would be opposed to this? Because I know what God has revealed and I've caught a glimpse of His character. Surely, my theologian interlocutors would agree. But what I've done is to rely on my intuition about matters not discussed in the text, as my intuition has been molded by the text. In this way, I can also make conclusions about a great many other things not specifically addressed in the text, such as, The Great Planned Plague, I'll later describe.

The point is that one cannot merely go on one's intuitions. How, in the name of Ignorantia, would those ridiculous theologians take that from what I'm saying? And you can be sure, my young friend, that I said everything to them that I'm saying now! . . . Forgive me. I need to calm myself. It's just that my whole venture is to point out that Ignorantian intuitions are indeed crooked and must be straightened . . . by the Word.

I suppose I'll end this for now, but you'll get more from this old babbler. Perhaps all this talk of romance and love has something to do with my personal matters. I'll let you in on this, Earnest: I'm courting a lady at the moment. Yes, yes, I'm too old. I'm well aware, but if that's what you're thinking, put it out of your mind. My beloved bride passed several years ago, and I've been heartbroken since. As best I can tell, Ms. Larkin is a true Verumian spirit. Looking at her is like looking in a mirror, to avoid the clichéd phrase, "soulmate." I'll keep you posted on how things develop!

Your friend and informant,
Solomon

PART TWO:

–

Dearest Solomon,

I long for more of your counsel and wisdom. It has been six months since I received your correspondence. You'll approve, I do hope, of my sharing your words with all of Verum. The Verumians were cut to the heart. We grieve over this revelation of affairs in Ignorantia. Day and night, all of Verum is interceding for your nation. It will not be long until I make the voyage, but your comments have provoked in me a desire for further preparation and study. Ignorantia must be a bastion of temptation and wickedness, shrouded in the language of freedom. Built on a faux foundation mistaken for biblical knowledge, the Ignorantia church is, for the most part, in a slumber. Why have I not received further correspondence? Your Verumian brothers and sisters are waiting. I am waiting.

Sanctified in Verum,

Earnest

LETTER FOUR
Politics

Young Earnest,

I received your correspondence, and am humbled you found my ramblings in some way profitable. It's always good to know one has Verum on one's side. So long have I been in writing to you this fourth time because . . . well . . . femininity has arrested my attention. I believe I mentioned Ms. Larkin in my last letter. She has me feeling like a bit of an infatuated schoolboy again. She's a rising local politician, and this is a difficult role for a lady who is a true Verumian soul. Moreover, we don't always see eye-to-eye. Don't fret, though, lad. It places me in a bit of an awkward position, I must say, yet we agree on the most central matters. You know, expressing the Ignorantian political situation may reveal itself to be a helpful thing, now that I consider it. The subject strikes back to our central discussion.

The Bible is a letter from God, and is the most important source of knowledge on the nature of reality, but just remember that politics and religion don't mix. A copy of the Bible is a must for the inauguration of an Ignorantian president, but what that president thinks about the "good book" should not sway a Christian vote. A quality clergyman will preach the whole counsel of God, but he'd best watch his tongue when it comes to matters of the state, lest we lose our tax-exemption.

Such are the sentiments of many an Ignorantian Christian. It is a manifestation of what I have oft referred to as, situational-atheism. Quietly, and perhaps more publically once per week, a sort of Christian Ignorantian views the Bible to be and contain the very riches of the eternal Creator. Its every page is imbued with the scent of the divine. He may not know its meaning, whether he knows if he knows it or not, but he reveres it with all sincerity. But, when he opens his morning copy of The Ignorantian Herald, he views the stories of kings, presidents, life, death, war, legality, sexuality, and all else in a more pragmatic manner. His quiet thoughts about the ancient text become more like his quiet thoughts about a hobby. It's not real or relevant in the way current events are real and relevant. He's not aware of this situational-atheism, this bifurcation of his worldview. For him, Christianity and spirituality come in and out of existence regularly. God becomes like a child's decorative mobile. It is mesmerizing and entrancing when it's before him, but when not the subject of his focus, it seems to fade into obscurity within his mind. For such a man, his opinions and statements about world events will betray little difference from the full-time secularist next door. The situational atheist, this mobile-man as we might think of him, is very real, but he's not the primary focus of our attention. Instead, we must turn to the mirror loving, community-molded, culture-bloated, grid-maker of the more conservative variety.

Our mobile-man is turned off, in a sense. He's not self-aware when it comes to his religious beliefs. He's downright inconsistent. And, in this regard, the self-aware Ignorantian believer has better footing. But politics is just another reason why the typical Ignorantian thinks he knows the Scriptures better than he does in fact. For him, it becomes a tangled mess. His half-formed intuitions have been augmented by a sort of nationalism. Themes and ideologies are presented throughout the Ignorantian culture, many of which are good. Particular views and party positions are reinforced by the community of his local congregation. Recall how I previously wrote to you regarding the toddler-man, and his absorption of the church culture. He views what those around him do, and associates this with the message of the Bible. In this way, political messages are smuggled into the Scriptures via the community, and the toddler-man drinks it in like mother's milk.

This purely mental and invisible version of the Bible intermingles with truncated scriptural teachings about love, judgementalism, forgiveness, animal life, war, poverty, the environment, and more. In some cases, a bit of the mosaic law is sprinkled in without covenantal caveat, and we're left with a party-specific rendering of the Bible. Which party? Any of them! All of them! As much as the words of Scripture are like text on a mirror, they are written on a flag or campaign poster.

Divisions in the church, therefore, often emerge along party lines. Sometimes this is done quietly, and occasionally it's obvious. And while all of this is circulating in the great and powerful nation of Ignorantia, it has allowed for certain exceedingly immoral and unbiblical institutions to emerge. One of those is what I obliquely called The Great Planned Plague. It is with a heavy heart, Earnest, that I write to you about this matter, and if you share these thoughts with your Verumian countrymen, they will undoubtedly cry out in grief. They may not believe it, for the idea that some misguided Christian Ignorantians would advocate for The Great Planned Plague will render them incredulous. In Ignorantia it is legal to kill unborn children prior to birth. Worse, in recent days infants are allowed to die shortly after birth. This is happening through programs funded by the Ignorantian government, and the killing has occurred in the millions. I'm quite sure my explanation has caused you to weep in terrible sorrow. It should. Set my letter down and take a moment to recover if you must, for what I must now tell you is worse still. Many Christian Ignorantians are speaking out, voting, and petitioning in favor of this horrendous movement of death.

The mobile-man, with his situational-atheism, never considers his quiet Christianity when thinking of politics. But the self-aware culture-bloater, with his invisible Bible, presents an array of explanations for his support. I'll discuss those presently, but first I must address an objection. Though you, my Verumian friend, with the darkness of this wickedness swirling in your mind, would never entertain the concept, some would challenge that my resistance of The Great Planned Plague is a symptom of my own invisible Bible. Have I taken the very misstep about which I here warn you? Am I imprinting my political ideas onto the pages of the text of an invisible Bible along party lines? God forbid!

The killing of children, born or unborn, is not a political issue. It is an issue that has been politicized. When an immoral position becomes part of a political ideology, it remains immoral. In such cases, the Bible, and the molded intuitions that arise from it should determine our views of politics. Our politics should not mold our intuitions or determine the meaning of the Bible.

The culture-bloated Christian, with his delicately twisted intuition, will agree that The Great Planned Plague is wicked, but he will refrain from saying so too loudly. He will take no action against the plague, and may even lend support. Why, you ask? Because of inverted-virtue. "What's that?" I imagine you to ask, and the imaginary you is asking a fair question, indeed. The culture-bloater agrees that we're talking about killing children here, but he points out that after all, it's not his place to tell others what to do. Matters are exacerbated by the otherwise wonderful focus on women's rights carrying on in Ignorantia. No man wishes to be found guilty of misogyny, tis among the greatest cultural sins these days. There is virtue in that, and as far as this goes, I'm happy to give the toddler-man my applause. Liberty is a virtue, and our man is aiming at virtuosity. Hear, hear! Nonetheless, life is a higher virtue, and both are in play. So how should our Christian Ignorantian progress? It's no difficult equation for those with properly molded intuitions. He should favor the virtue of life over the virtue of liberty. Sadly, because of his culturally distorted intuitions, our virtue-seeking fellow reverses the two and is left with inverted-virtue. The act is a killing, but the act should be free. After all, Ignorantia is a free country. Is this how the common Ignorantian would judge the private act of one neighbor killing another? Inconsistencies abound.

Some Christian Ignorantians even attempt to argue from the Bible itself, usually citing that Adam was not a living being until he had breath in his lungs. Quite right, quite right – I'm sure you're amazed at the foolishness. Adam was a formed physical structure of dust prior to the granting of life. Quite right, if you're thinking the breath of life does not refer to mere oxygen. Quite right, that even if it were, oxygen is present in the blood of a child. Quite right, quite right! Now settle down, my companion. I'm sure my words have worked you up. I know all too well that the twisting of Scripture has a chilling effect on the Verumian mind. Only partially better is what they do with Exodus 21:22-25.

Scripture has it,

> *If men struggle with each other and strike a woman with child so that she gives birth prematurely, yet there is no injury, he shall surely be fined as the woman's husband may demand of him, and he shall pay as the judges decide. But if there is any further injury, then you shall appoint as a penalty life for life, eye for eye, tooth for tooth, hand for hand, foot for foot, burn for burn, wound for wound, bruise for bruise.*

Now, you likely do not see the problem here, Earnest, and I sympathize. For Ignorantians, the phrase, "gives birth prematurely," is taken to refer to the killing of an unborn child. Why? Some translations instead have it, "miscarriage." Since the penalty is only a fine, and not life for life justice, it's understood by the Ignorantian to mean that God does not consider the unborn child to be a life. You must understand that Ignorantians are generally lazy. They can't be bothered to consult the original language. If they did, the problem would resolve itself. The word for "miscarriage" is יצא yatsa' and literally means to "come out." Contextually, the meaning is usually in relation to a live birth, as in Genesis 25:25, "the first came out red, all of him like a hairy robe; and they called his name Esau." Now, if Moses wished to convey the idea of a miscarriage, there seems to be a better word at his disposal. Moses uses another word for miscarriage just two chapters later: "None shall lose her young by miscarriage or be barren in your land" (Exodus 23:26, AMP). The word used here is שכל 'shakol', and is often translated as "miscarriage" in modern translations. The Ignorantian case falls flat. But oh, should you see what they do with the purity ritual of Numbers 5:11-22.

There, as you know, we see the actions to be taken if a man suspects his wife has been unfaithful to him. He brings her before the priests where she will agree to a potential priestly curse that if she has been unfaithful will cause her "abdomen to swell" and her "thigh" to "waste away." She will drink water that has been sprinkled with a pinch of dust from the floor of the tabernacle. The priests carry on with some other trappings and the entire party will, I presume, wait and see what happens. Strange as this ceremony appears to modern eyes, it is not at all similar to the actions taken by those involved in The Great Planned Plague. There is nothing about the killing of a child, and the whole business is a religious ceremony, not a medical treatment. Moreover, if one doubts the efficacy of curses and rituals, the woman is in safe keeping. A bit of dust from the floor of the tabernacle will do no harm, and if it did, the whole encampment would be in jeopardy. One may not like the humiliation of this business, but that neither makes it immoral nor an example of the plague. Ignorantians will be Ignorantian, after all. And it should be no surprise at this point in our communication that their use of Scripture is thoroughly Ignorantian.

My meaning is not to focus on merely one issue, but to illustrate the degree to which this whole business of unmolded intuitions and culture-bloat has impacted even the otherwise faithful of our land. But, it's only fair to the chosen of God to grant that a great many of them still resist The Great Planned Plague. For them we may cheer with unfettered enthusiasm, but the whole of the Ignorantian church exists on a spectrum. While these are closer to the truth, they too make common missteps as a result of this political obsession.

The Great Planned Plague is wicked enough to prevent many Christian Ignorantians from ever supporting a politician who is in support of the movement. This forces most of them into only one remaining party. My hat is off to them. The problem is that they then experience the culture-bloat of that political party and marry it with their theological beliefs. Like all other toddler-men, they observe the views of those around them and do likewise. Other issues come prepackaged with the party, and not all of those are obviously good. It is not uncommon for these culture-bloaters to take on apathetic views regarding man's concern for the environment, for instance. Some even utter, in hushed tones, that because the grid tells them the end is nigh, why bother trying to protect creation. Yes! I've heard of the beautiful Verumian gardens – your hanging vines, and ample fruit trees. I hope to one day eat of the Verumian Voavanga, and lie between the manicured rainbow leaf plums. You are known for your appreciation of what the hand of God has planted.

What I fear you'll deduce is a sort of contradiction in my thoughts. Am I reasoning toward an inverted-virtue in my own position? If life should trump liberty, shouldn't it also trump environmentalism? Indeed! I'm not arguing for an embrace of some political party that supports The Great Planned Plague in a sad attempt to protect non-cognitive creation. Of course not! I'm arguing for Christians to think independently. One does not need to support a political party in order to remain faithful to the Kingdom, but if one does, one does not need to take on all the views of that party like an automaton. I'm arguing against the toddler-man's embrace of the common group-think. I'm raging against his mixing patriotism to Ignorantia and patriotism to the Kingdom in equal measure. I'm certainly battling an unnoticed ideology that confuses national sentiment with Bible verses, and constitutions with epistles. When such occurs, the Ignorantian begins to think, "surely the Bible says," when the Bible does not, and "God is for this," when God is not.

Forgive me. After my last paragraph I had to stand and pace the room to calm myself. When I did, I caught a glimpse of my dear Ms. Larkin at the other end of the street. She'll be here soon. You know, Earnest, I would request your prayer, but please don't inform your Verumian brothers.

Ms. Larkin and I are at odds on some of this. As a voice for the people, she feels impressed to support the entire slate of positions held by her party. Perhaps that is why I've just become so rattled. I say she is a Verumian spirit, and I do mean that, Earnest, you must believe me. Still, she has talked herself into a small amount of culture-bloat, but it's only a small amount. And as for me, I must recognize that there is something about love that opens one's mind to the ideas of one's other. Pray for me that I may be wise in this. Previously I had not noticed the degree to which affection can begin to peel away strongly held convictions. One wishes to be in agreement with one's partner, and a dab of oxytocin, with a smidge of romantic longing goes a long way in seducing the mind.

Don't worry too much though, my loyal correspondent. She's not much of a culture-bloater, and weak-minded as I am, for I am an Ignorantian after all, I'm wise enough to resist. My heart may be spinning, but my virtues are not inverted.

Your friend and informant,
Solomon

-
-
-
-
-
-
-
-
-
-
-
-
-
-
-
-
-
-
-
-
-
-
-
-
-
-
-
-

LETTER FIVE
Sallow Spires

Earnest,

Because of your concern for my lateness in response, I hurried off with my thoughts on politics. I didn't want you to worry over this old rambler. However, I have now been late again. It's been several months since I last wrote, and I'm confident that if I do not put ink to parchment soon, you will worry all the more, and draft another anxious letter. So here I am, sitting in a high sallow spire above the sea. The sky scraper, as these structures are called, houses the political offices of my dear Ms. Larkin. For me, it serves as a tower of Babel for a bona fide babbler.

I should let you know that Ms. Larkin and I have recently been wed, though she retains her surname for reason of publicity. In an instant, I was displaced from my quiet modest home, and now spend my time in the finest of Ignorantian hotels, restaurants, lounges, and theatres. You see, no sooner did we marry, than did my wife rocket to the pinnacle of acclaim. It happened swiftly as political celebrity sometimes does. With my bride I have houses, and at my disposal are vineyards, gardens, parks and fruit trees. We have men and women who serve our every need and are employed by us. We have the finest in all things. There is enough silver and gold to satisfy a king. And as for entertainment, we have singers and musicians on-call. In fact, I myself have ridden these matrimonial coattails and have taken up a cause all my own. I plan to construct what I call the Ignorantian Institute for Intellectual Interests, or I. I. I. I.

I imagine you looking at the page with suspicion, dear friend, but roll your eyes no more. Verumians would not approve of my crafty plan, but it represents a subtle attempt to subvert the culture. I'll begin a think-tank for resolving the Ignorantian problems of our day. We'll hold seminars. We'll discuss the great books of the Western world. When appropriate, a study of the Bible as literature will be had. We'll call the lecture series, MEtanarratives MEaningful for MEmbers of a MEnding MEtropolis. We may even offer MEdallions for those who faithfully attend. Now, this is where my subversion will reach its peak, and I have to grant that as I'm writing these things down, I am salivating at the thought of it. I'll have to preach the Ignorantian message the way they want to hear it, at least at first. I know, I know. You are shifting in your seat. The very thought of it boils your Verumian blood. But, perhaps the reason I've been ignored til now is because I was too bold, and too forthright. Maybe that's why the Ignorantian theologians brushed me off. That's what my bride seems to think. Eventually, and I hope this will redeem my intentions for you, I will turn the teaching from the Ignorantian sort to the true and good message of God's Word. They will come to know the Bible itself. My students will be the seeds from which we may grow a vast Verumian society of Bible lovers here within Ignorantia. I'll have to teach that which I do not believe at first, but as they say, the ends will justify the means.

Meanwhile, Earnest, I'll have to publicly lend support for the political positions of my bride. I suppose I might as well let this one out. Part of Ms. Larkin's campaign is support for The Great Planned Plague. It has been the greatest source of frustration in our relationship. Why did I marry her in spite of this? Romantic love. You likely don't know its power, Earnest, and powerful it is! I'll lend her my support, and endorse the plague in interviews, and news articles, but oh how I'll hate every minute. Yet, recall that my endorsing it is out of a sense of loyalty to my love, and furthermore, it will keep me in good standing with our donors who will, in turn, fund the I. I. I. I. and make possible the ME. ME. ME. ME. ME. study, through which I will eventually teach them to properly learn Scripture and think for themselves. And certainly, I'll continue to enjoy the many benefits of my new social status. I cannot be blamed for the fine wine, extravagant home, or lavish holidays. It's all part of the subversion. God has surely placed me here for the task just articulated. As for my plan to preach Ignorantian falsehood, and endorse Ignorantian violence, I'm confident He'll give me a pass. These are necessary evils for defeating Ignorantian ones.

I've no doubt that Verumians would consider my flirtation with thoroughly Ignorantian evils and doctrines to be dangerous. You would all contend, "You shall not associate with them, for they will surely turn your heart away!" Yes, yes, yes. I'm well aware. But you must know, young man, that I'm in a sui generis situation here. Conceivably, resolving Ignorantian society will require one to get one's hands dirty. Naturally, I'm just the man for the mission! My knowledge of their tactics is unparalleled. As I've illustrated in my writings to you, I know what these cosmopolites are up to better than they! Please know that I wish I could pass this cup on to someone else. It's is a weighty load.

As I sit here drinking the fruit of the finest Ignorantian vines, and absorbing the most aged and odorous Ignorantian cheeses, I realize that this must be my cross to bear. Someone must do it, and I expect I'll have to be the one to take it on the chin. Do not suspect that I prefer this life. Oh, naturally, I can't help but enjoy the finer things. I previously said so, did I not? However, an Ignorantian is currently working on my pedicure, and another is playing the violin just now. My constant awareness that they are imbeciles who could never keep pace with men like us, brings a great sorrow to my heart. Oh, they've just brought my dinner in. I think it's caviar tonight, with a flute of spirits. It's a bit of a cliché scene I'm describing to you, Earnest, but thank God. Yes, thank God indeed, that I'm willing to make this sacrifice instead of you. Why, a lesser man surely would be turned away by such amenities. I, on the contrary, can stand strong. Worry not, my friend. I will not be so influenced as to waver in my hidden mission. Forget the cautionary tales, I will not.

In our land of mega-churches, there are those men desirous of this sort of a lifestyle. They wish to live it out unapologetically. I'm speaking here of some well-known Ignorantian preachers. They alter their messages in order to get a large hearing. Their congregations grow, and so do their bank accounts. Having gotten what they want, these sheep-clothed wolves promise lives of financial excess to their followers. Health and wealth and all that Ignorantian jazz. They know they're lying, and they never stop. It's a real problem. But surely you can't put me in that box, young Earnest.

My intentions are not to amass or maintain wealth. That may be a perk, or occupational hazard, but my motivation is to say what they want to hear only as long as necessary. Once I have a following, I'll scrub off the sugar coating, and give it to them straight. I'm like a spy behind enemy lines, and surely such operatives are necessary.

If my tone seems altogether different from what you've read of me in the past, there's a very good reason. I think back on my comments to you and I know they are the truth, but I was a complainer. I was a mere whiner. At this moment, I'm a man on a mission. If I sound at all arrogant in my aspirations, I do not apologize. Without a bit of self-confidence, how could a soldier progress? Am I self-assured? Naturally! After all, do not my uniquely rewarding circumstances testify that I am pleasing to the Father?

So, when you are tempted to return word to me, just realize that I already know what you'll say. I love you, dear boy, but the last thing I require is to be lectured by a Verumian youth. Isn't it my whole point to prepare you for what this land is like? You know it not. I do! I'm the master, and you are the learner! Just remember that!

I'm sorry, Earnest. After that last line, I prayed for forgiveness. It was a peaceful moment to do so, anyhow. The masseuse came 'round, and I had her work my back while I humbly repented. I've left the paragraph, for the point is well made, but I shouldn't have been so hard on you. Perhaps you wouldn't have criticized my plan or predicament after all. Verumians are remarkably intelligent, and you are among their best. Lesser citizens of even Verum may question my motives, but not you. You're too smart for that. You'll see the brilliance in this. You'll recognize the divine hand at work. Thank you, my friend. Thank you for what I know your response will be. Now, I've got to head off to a late-night gathering. They're serving a bit of blood pudding, and get this – it's plated in edible golden flakes! Have you ever heard of such a thing? What will these Ignorantians next devise?

Your friend and informant,

Solomon

LETTER SIX
Twists

Earnest,

Do not the best of tales upend the reader's expectations? Is it false to suggest that the best of desserts is complex and layered? Am I wrong, or isn't it true that lovers find far greater treasures in knowing the person rather than seeing the body? I point all of this out, Earnest, because I've stumbled onto a method for impacting the Ignorantian mind that buries the lead, as it were. If you protested my previous diatribe, you'll flat denounce the approach I presently articulate, but I'll try to convince your primitive Verumian spirit all the same. Oh, I hope that doesn't sound condescending, I do love Verum, as I love all backwater fundamentalists. You people are the salt of the earth, and surely, I value your opinions or I'd cease writing.

It's now been another six months, and the I. I. I. I. is off and running. I've even begun the ME. ME. ME. ME. ME. course ahead of schedule. Funding is rolling in, and I have garnered the attention, and involvement of the leaders of various sects of Ignorantian Christianity, as well as law-makers and secular university professors. Not bad for such a short space of the year. I've been influenced, Earnest, by these Ignorantians. I was wrong. There are some truly brilliant leaders here who understand all I've said about grids, cultures, intuitions, and politics, but they have a deeper plan. I'll elucidate the key elements.

First, the Christian Ignorantian leaders I've been talking with want to impact the culture with the Bible by concealing the Bible, at least at first. Now I know what you're thinking, but maybe there's something to it. The culture at large rejects the Bible, and even some Christian Ignoranitans find blunt declarations from Scripture to be cringe-inducing, at best, and distasteful at least. Nevertheless, there are a great many non-Christian literary masterpieces, films, and musical compilations that play indirectly on obvious Christian themes. Forgiveness, redemption, courage, and endurance. One changes a nation best by affecting its stories. By using the organizations at our disposal to encourage education in just these sorts of resources, we will teach the Scriptures without teaching the Scriptures. Once the culture has been thoroughly steeped in Christian ideals, including those most hospitable to proper doctrinal positions, our I. I. I. I. will pull back the curtain and reveal to all Ignorantia that they have been imbibing in the sacred texts without even realizing. By that point, the culture will already have shifted, and the adoption of the truth will come easily. Why didn't I see it before, Earnest! The Christian Ignorantians have been thoroughly Ignorantian, but their framers have been craftier than I ever thought. And perhaps I've been wrong about politics too.

Now that I know the quiet conspiracy, I can see that the parties in play are important for shaping the culture. Each bureaucratic faction has its problems, but we have to endorse the high principles of the truth in a way that goes down easily. That's how it will best be accepted over a long period of time. By controlling the culture, and with political manipulation, we'll secure the sort of society for which we strive. Now all of this requires money, and that money comes from our religious organizations and denominations. Congregants give to those organizations because they accept the theological grids, and cultural norms of them. This is why - and I can't imagine that it didn't occur to me before - the individual sects train people in grids and cultures instead of training individuals to seriously consider the grids of other sects and denominations. For some, and certainly not all, it is because they must ensure long-term allegiance to a particular sect for financial stability. This, in-turn, is vital to the funding of organizations like the I. I. I. I. It really does come down to money, Earnest. I know how that sounds, but money can be a useful tool. And I know you won't fall into the typical Ignorantian trap of presuming that money is the root of all evil. You know that the Apostle really taught that it was the love thereof, that was the problem.

Yes, we'll continue to endorse the grids that I previously wrote against. We'll endorse the culture-bloat, and pacify the toddler-man. We shall grow richer and richer still, but we'll do it all to the glory of the Father, though not in His name, at least not at first. We'll twist the Scriptures, but only a little. We'll keep the Bible to ourselves, but only for a while. And I know with all knowing that you Verumians will detest all of this, but the situation is complex. Take heart, my dear friend, that our theologians will go on theologizing, and our churches will go on churching all the same.

We'll have to combine our intentions with national patriotism in order to motivate the movement, and it may well be that in the end some will confuse the cross and the flag, but desperate times call for desperate measures. This is a tangled dilemma, and it is a multifaceted evangelistic endeavor. But just imagine it in the end, dear Earnest, when the curtain is pulled away, and the Bible is seen to be the engine behind all that Ignoroantia has grown to love. Conceive of it, my Verumian friend! It will be like the greatest of all upendings! It will be the twist of all twists. And we can do it, I have no doubt. Perhaps, by leaving our Bibles in the churches where only the faithful will see them, they will have the most tremendous effect! By never uttering the name of Jesus, we'll please Him the most! I know how it sounds, young missionary, but the prescribed medication will take! I just know it! I can feel it in my blood!

This leads me to my final comments, Earnest, and I hope you'll take them onboard. You should not come to Ignorantia. There, I said it. You should stay in sweet Verum. The flat, straightforward preaching of the gospel no longer works as it once did. Even as I began to craft my first letters to you I functioned as you surely do now. I went about with the Bible in hand, and the Savior on my lips. I was a missionary to my own country, and feared not to speak of sin, hell, damnation, and salvation. The cross was a symbol of redemption, and I wanted everyone to see it as it was, and hear it in its own biblical terms. One day, a new generation may see that freedom again.

For now, I'll continue suffering through the dinner parties, and fancy homes. I'll experience the martyrdom of materialism as my pockets are lined with the fruit of my silence. This lavish existence is a true pain, Earnest, and how fortunate you are that I'm facing the sacrifice for you. If you came to Ignorantia, as we had initially planned, they'd likely seduce you. I can manage with one eye on the secret goal, but you could not. Moreover, you'd find yourself ineffective. The old methods are no longer successful. Stay where you are lad! Stay in Verum and pray for our plan.

Do not expect to hear from me again, Earnest. Perhaps one day I'll meet you on that Verumian shore, with throngs of Verumian brothers. On that day, I can tell you all about how I saved a nation in the most unexpected way. You don't understand now, my correspondent, but you will by and by. You'll see, you'll see. The change of heart comes slowly, but in the end, it is liberating.

Now I must be off, the local community is presenting me with an award for my work and community excellence. I hear tell that even the president of all Ignorantia is going to transmit a message in my honor. All it took was keeping the Bible out of the limelight. That's all I ever need to do, in order to make the biggest impact. Greet the Verumians dear brother, and tell them simply that

God is smiling on their weary wealthy wordy worker!

Your friend and informant,
Solomon

PART THREE:

–

Woe unto you Solomon, for you have been led astray! Your words were dripping with the nectar of truth, until you married a woman whose heart was far from it. Vanity has coaxed you into a snare! You have traded the savior for silver, and the gospel for gold. You have deceived yourself, and in your own words, "The man who is deceived does not know he has been deceived or he never would have been deceived." You who were wisest of all, have become the clearest expression of the danger of which you sought to warn – the ignorance of the Word of God!

LETTER SEVEN:
Snares

To the happy hostage,

I learned from your pen, Solomon, and was trained from afar. As your pupil, my mind was broadened. So now, my mentor, I shall provoke you with a letter, that in some way I might stir up the man I once knew. May conviction spill out on you as a torrent, and shame like a sea. It can't be denied that I grew angry at your regress, but this indignation is mingled with love. Know it, Solomon! Believe it, for it is true!

Your mind, oh Solomon, is like unto a classic work, a celebrated masterpiece set out of reach on the highest shelf. It appears glorious and would be ever useful, but is closed and now benign. You are like a skilled violinist, unparalleled in his abilities, but who only scratches at the strings. What have you become, wayward brother? Your schemes are alien, and your plots offensive. Hearken to me, now!

How may I string your violin that you might play once more? It is your duty. Or do you not know the Evangelist Luke? Has Ignorantia erased the memory of his gospel? The servant who knew his master's will, but grew drunk and gluttonous all the same, shall be cut into pieces. Our Lord, even your Lord, demands, "From everyone who has been given much, much will be required; and to whom they entrusted much of him they will ask all the more." (Luke 12:48) You are the man! You have grown gluttonous, and have become a drunkard.

Think, dear brother! Think! Upon a stump, as a humble hermit, you were a master of your instrument. Few would ever hear, but the music rang true, and beautiful. I could have listened for hours as you worked the strings. On one enchanting day, a Delilah intoxicated you. Suddenly you were on a stage in some grand concert hall. The world was watching, and the pieces were set. Did you play for them as you had on your stump? You did not! You gave them the scratching of strings. You gave them abomination. You gave them what they wanted. So odd it is that what does not even sound like music to my Verumian ears, they consider complex, and refined. What urges my skin to crawl, soothes them. You could have done it, Solomon! You could have showed them the music of David! With no effort, you could have unleashed the sound of eternity! For this, you are guilty. Much was given, and much is required.

It's clear to me, my former master, that there must be others like you in Ignorantia. Surely, others have traded a song for a screech. And I will seek them out, and make them sorrowful with my words. The preachers, and the pastors, and the writers, and the theologians, and all the string-scratchers who know the Verumian way, must repent of their screeching. It won't come easy, I see. We Verumians love discipline and correction, for we also love knowledge. But when one preaches an Ignorantian sermon, writes an Ignorantian book, or presents an Ignoranian lecture, pride prevents a Verumian corrective – pride and greed. Once one has skin in the game, he can hardly change his words. If he does, it will reveal that he was wrong. What then? What if his Ignorantian congregation leaves him? Perhaps his Ignorantian readers will stop reading. Those who buy grids from the theologian gridmakers will look elsewhere. Where will the Ignorantian Christian leaders get their silver and gold? Thus, the preachers, pastors, writers, and theologians continue as string-scratchers. Maybe they learn to like the sound of their own scraping.

My purpose is clear, and my task resolute. You, sad Solomon, wrote to tell me how a nation comes to believe they know a Bible they do not. I write to tell you how a man who knows the Bible forgets it! A subtle trap has been triggered, and you're in its teeth. Perhaps, just perhaps, even now its jaws may be pried away. I'm prying my best, brother! God knows I am! I'll begin with seduction, and we Verumians do know something of that.

In presuming that we Verumians know little of Ignorantia, a point about which you are correct, you have assumed we know nothing of life. We are not prudes, and we are not naïve. The enticement of the opposite sex is not foreign to us. Though I am young, I know the power of the curve of a hip, breath on the ear, and the friction of skin. I know the pleasure found in a woman who cares to listen to a man's ideas. These delights are not the property of Ignorantians. They occur in Verum, but we humbly manage our urges. We are a wild, but holy tribe! You were seduced, and I do not refer explicitly to sex. You were seduced by a woman in what seemed the most innocent of ways. It was a seduction of attention, as much as femininity. Someone seemed to care that you exist.

It happens all over Ignorantia, I've no doubt, when men and women who love the Word marry and forget. "Do not play those songs," the new Ignorantian spouses must insist. "Play with the satisfying tones of Ignorantia, my dear. It will become natural in time." And they play while their Rome is slowly burning. I'm sure I'll see it all when I land on your Ignorantian shores.

You wrote to me, Solomon, of politics, but you have become the politician. The seduction led you to campaign, and the campaign demanded total allegiance. Now, dear fellow, your intuitions have been altered. No longer are they molded by Scripture. The intuition mold sits high atop a shelf too. You have molded your intuition device to your own image, and you're following it wherever it may lead. Is it not fascinating how quickly the mental-migration is undone? In so little time you have forgotten your way.

This is how it always is, and there is a great mystery to the thing. To study the Word is a discipline. If it is not regularly practiced, one's knowledge recedes. So many less important things stay with us without effort, like the ability to read or ride a bicycle, but the most important of information slips away with great rapidity. Is this not evidence of spiritual warfare? I can only imagine it must be. It must be practiced, but you have given it up. You wrote to me of words on a mirror, the interpretation of Scripture on the backdrop of our own images. Nevertheless, you have given up words altogether. You do not gaze on yourself as you gaze at the Scriptures. You gaze on yourself alone.

Seduction brought you to the construction of an organization where you could teach your own thoughts. Seduction brought you to a table of excess. Lust twisted your intentions, and you allowed it to wash over you. Like so many, you pretended it was acceptable. In your letters, you excused yourself. How many have done the same? Do all Ignorantian brothers excuse their sins and call it enlightenment? I wonder. May it be that one day some hapless Ignorantian will read these words and consider what sins exist in his own life. Perhaps he will acknowledge that he has made excuse.

Excuses find reinforcement in the culture-bloat, Solomon. You are quite bloated, indeed. Viewing Ignorantia through your words, as if by a scope, I see it all so clear. When a man falls into a sinful snare, and cannot shake it off, he associates with others, ensnared in a like manner. They become a community of Ignorantians moving up and down the street, in and out of shops, with the equivalents of bear traps clasped around their ankles – teeth beneath the skin. Each dragging their own snares, limping as they go, they conduct their business, and attend dinner parties. As Verumian spirits look on them with confusion, and try to convince them of their maladies, they speak with baffling condescension. They've grown to love their snares. They decorate them, compare them, and pity those who do not have them. All the while they are slowly dying.

These ensnared men and women, who knew the Scriptures best, find security in the community. They look around them and say, "Ah, this must be the truly enlightened spirituality." Regressed, they have, back to the toddler. In such a state, and with such biblical knowledge, the twisting, and grid-crafting becomes most intricate. Men who know the Bible the best, and fall in with men who live it the least, are capable of twisting Scripture softly, which is truly the worst.

Hearken to me, Solomon! Woe unto you, grid-twister! Woe unto you, culture-bloater! You have become the toddler-man! With your marred intuition, you have landed yourself in the nearly-way! I weep for my wayward teacher. He has become the string-scratcher, so may he listen to my warning! You, oh Solomon, have done it - that which I'd never have expected! You have become a true Ignorantian!

Sanctified in Verum,

Earnest

LETTER EIGHT:
Comfort

To the sated sinner,

Verily, verily, I say to you, Solomon, you speak as a man who has forgotten his own name. "God must be pleased for I am prosperous!" Foolish words! Could not every wealthy sinner, and each wicked dictator utter the same? The Ignorantian assumes the Creator is on his side because excess is had. Every cult leader says as much. "My followers are growing. I've found the true way." Riches do not prove divine acclaim. Foxes have holes, and the birds of the air have nests, but the Son of Man hath not where to lay his head.

It was the fear of your theologians, the ones who tossed you out of the halls, that if they entertained your thoughts they might lose their positions. Now you understand them, and make the same error. How often it must be that an Ignorantian fears to change his mind on some point of doctrine. What pain there must be in pointing out error among those who provide one's comfort. If a pastor knows in his heart that the group is teaching error on this issue or that, would not he lose his standing and position to make the proclamation? Would this not, in turn, rend his security and comfort?

Verily, verily I say to you, Solomon, Christian themes are not enough. Some famous Ignorantian is supposed to have said, "Preach the gospel, and if necessary use words." To Ignorantian ears, such notions sound artful, but to Verumians they are nonsense. The gospel is information passed on by clear communication. It was not for a theme that the martyrs shed their blood. Living a life that testifies to the truth of the message is vital, but concealing the message is damning. You spoke of changing the culture by infusing biblical ideas. You wrote of leaving the Bibles in the churches and subtly speaking through films and music and books. Let me tell you how a once literate nation becomes illiterate, and how the most eloquent of speakers becomes mute. Plagiarism is a dastardly thing.

There once was a man who had two friends, a farmer and an art professor. The professor thought the farmer to be a tasteless brute who knew nothing of creative expression. But the farmer was, in fact, a brilliant painter. Our mutual companion daily attempted to convince the arrogant teacher of the artistic merits found in the farmer's brush. The professor would not hear it. In an attempt to demonstrate the point, the mutual friend stole away one of the paintings from the farmer's barn, and sold it to a gallery at a high price. He did this anonymously so the farmers reputation would not impact the judgement. Soon the masterful work was praised, most of all by the professor who drooled over it in his lectures. Seeing the acceptance of the piece, and fearing that the farmer's name would lessen the impact it was having on the art world, the mutual friend never revealed the creator. When the farmer finally appeared with a new painting just as dazzling as the first, he was seen as a cheap copyist or pretender.

What the community would never know, is that the simple work they had so praised was only a taste. It was the least of what was on offer. Though it nears impossible to accept, the farmer's barn was filled with works so ineffable, that had his name ever been known, and his true treasures revealed, the majesty of his creations would overshadow the history of artistic expression. All past and future art would be measured by his matchless designs.

Hearken to me, Solomon, for our Lord is like the farmer, and you and your culture-bloaters are like the mutual friend. Plagiarists you are! You present the work of the master in films of redemption, and books of forgiveness, but you have presented these goods anonymously. So long has the plagiarism been in progress that the culture of Ignorantia likely does not realize that their entire society, morality, and list of virtues is built on a bastardization of the Christian message. That message, so surprising and rich to its first hearers, is now thought to be the copy. It is not the copy. And worse, the fullest expression of the artist's hand - his greatest impact - is shrouded in anonymity. His name must be declared!

You and your fellow Christian Ignorantians plan to prepare society with Christian principles, to prepare the way of the Lord and his book, but you fail to see the inevitable. By the time the book is revealed, the Ignorantians will think these virtues to be their own creations. They will not recognize the Bible as the source. You'll have only made matters the worse. In truth, because they did not have the intuition mold of the Bible itself, they will think it perverse when they read the page. You, yourself, described the key elements in your own hand. Awake, oh Solomon! Awake!

Verily, verily, I say to you, Solomon, the combination of nationalism and Christianity cements the delusion. You had it right at the first, but you have forgotten what you once knew. You have forgotten because your comfortable position has lulled you as if in a cradle. A city had a wise judge. All who knew him praised his great intellect. Citizens heard his words, and the city flourished. The judge wrote a book, and news of his wisdom spread afar. In a distant frontier, noble thinkers took the book to be a helpful guide in the organization of a new world. Years later the blossoming settlement was divided between two factions. Each group longed for some goods and some evils. Each group pointed to the book, and claimed that the old judge would have agreed with them. "Surely, he'd have been among our ranks!" In time, the true message of the judge would be lost, along with the secrets of a flourishing society. The citizenry would, invariably, give up on the book, and the perhaps mythological judge. Instead, they would adopt a marred new national religion, built loosely on his teaching, but without foundation. Perhaps my parable needs no explanation. Surely, Solomon, you are not so deluded that you would miss my meaning. If so, then the explanation of it would be of no use. I refuse to explain what should be plain.

As the Apostle Peter once wrote, "Therefore, I will always be ready to remind you of these things, even though you already know them," for you wrote of them to me, my deluded friend. I seek to teach you nothing, but to call you to bend a penitent knee. If you will not hear me, then may some similarly deluded Ignorantian accept my message. Are you fearful to move about with a Bible in your hand? Does the name of Jesus sound too cliché to a post-Christian land? Do you cringe at the concept of revealing the name of the painter, or pointing to the book of the great judge? Are you so embarrassed of your Lord that you sooth yourself with the lie that extreme subtlety is enlightened, and sophisticated? God forbid! Subtly and allegory are useful tools, but they are not enough. The gospel is the power of God unto salvation.

You have grown comfortable, Solomon! In your comfort you are sleeping. There is no one left for whom your Christless message is offensive. This should have been the first sign of calamity. Those who control your destiny would never abide your former words. Awake, sleeping Solomon! Awake!

Sanctified in Verum,

Earnest

LETTER NINE
Pride

To the witless wise man,

We have prayed for you, Solomon, since receiving your last communication, and I have preached hard to you twice without response. I urged the Verumians to wait until one final letter to Ignorantia had been sent, but they were filled with sorrow at your words. They could not resist but wished to make a lesson of your tale, as Verumians always long for opportunities to teach the truth. They have erected a monument in your name. It rests in our gardens among the hanging vines, and ample fruit trees. It is positioned between the manicured rainbow leaf plums where the voavanga flourish. Your image is the centerpiece of a shallow reflecting pond, a statue that appears to be lying on a watery mirror. Prostrate, are you there, made of immovable stone. Your face is in your hands as you rest impossibly upon your own reflection. If one could see the pond from above, the words of Scripture would be visible just beneath the surface, chiseled in stone by the most skilled of Verumian craftsmen. I will share it with you now, that collection of verses to which your immortal likeness clings, but first I must make my meaning plain. You are a true Ignorantian after all. The words of Scripture are now lost on you.

Pride was your downfall, my former teacher. In my letters, I have outlined symptoms and diagnosed you from afar; still, the core of your illness is your imperiousness. The secret to knowing the Bible as a Verumian is realizing how little of it one really does know. The deeper one swims into the depths of the divine, the deeper it seems to grow, and no man can reach its floor. We strive for it with a longing ineffable, living by the useful fiction that one day we will have the perfect grid, culture, intuition, and kingdom. We strive to be perfect as our Father in heaven is perfect. But the fiction will one day cease. When the Savior, whom you have hidden, arrives in Verum, he will sit on the grassy mounds and expound the revelation. You thought you knew it all, Solomon! And in knowing it, you despised the counsel of brothers. In knowing it you felt its laws did not apply, that you were a special case. You are not!

Pretension prevented your repentance. What would people think? And a hundred famous theologians must suffer from the same pretense. Your superciliousness served as insurance that the great Solomon would not return to his violin and play, once more, the song of salvation. The community had transformed you into a fat, pampered, pacified, toddler-man. But the toddler is dressed as a scholar. What a turn! What a marvel! What a curiosity! What a joke!

Loftiness was born out of love or lust or longing or all of these. The enemy knew your weakness, and he played on it with attention. Someone looked on you with appreciation. Love of her or love of self, muted conviction and lured you away. Such a perfect ploy! Such a subtle trap.

Let no Ignorantian who may stumble across these letters misunderstand. All you revealed about grids, and cultures, and intuitions, and politics is valuable and true. Useful, it was, and I'll need that knowledge as I travel to your land. When your belly was full, that was the change. As you were clothed in riches, the deception took root. In the end, dear brother, I hope you will repent. Perhaps you will not become the stone image lying on the reflecting pool. If he had a heart at all, it would be a heart of stone.

I can see it now as I sit on the hillside looking down on the creation. Beneath the waters the saddest of words may clearly be seen. It reads,

> *I said to myself, "Come now, I will test you with pleasure. So enjoy yourself." And behold, it too was futility. I said of laughter, "It is madness," and of pleasure, "What does it accomplish?" I explored with my mind how to stimulate my body with wine while my mind was guiding me wisely, and how to take hold of folly, until I could see what good there is for the sons of men to do under heaven the few years of their lives. I enlarged my works: I built houses for myself, I planted vineyards for myself; I made gardens and parks for myself and I planted in them all kinds of fruit trees; I made ponds of water for myself from which to irrigate a forest of growing trees. I bought male and female slaves and I had homeborn slaves. Also I possessed flocks and herds larger than all who preceded me in Jerusalem. Also, I collected for myself silver and gold and the treasure of kings and provinces. I provided for myself male and female singers and the pleasures of men—many concubines. Then I became great and increased more than all who preceded me in Jerusalem. My wisdom also stood by me. All that my eyes desired I did not refuse them. I did not withhold my heart from any pleasure, for my heart was pleased because of all my labor and this was my reward for all my labor. Thus I considered all my activities which my hands had done and the labor which I had exerted, and*

behold all was vanity and striving after wind and there was no profit under the sun. Ecclesiastes 2:1-11

Sanctified in Verum,

Earnest

Made in the USA
Coppell, TX
18 March 2022

75200848R00059